D0280726

WITHDRAWN

Please return on or before the latest date above.
You can renew online at www.kent.gov.uk/libs
or by phone 08458 247 200

CUSTOMER SERVICE EXCELLENCE

Libraries & Archives

By Donavan Christopher

CABOODLE BOOKS LTD

A Catalogue record for this book is available from
the British Library.

ISBN-13: 978-0-9562656-1-6

Typeset in Century Gothic by Paul Wilson

Printed in the UK by CPI Cox & Wyman, Reading

The paper and board used in the paperback by Caboodle
Books Ltd are natural recyclable products made from wood
grown in sustainable forests. The manufacturing processes
conform to the environmental regulations of the country of
origin.

Caboodle Books Ltd
Riversdale, 8 Rivock Avenue, Steeton, BD20 6SA, UK.
Tel: +44 (0)1535 656015

FOREWORD

Thank you to all who have shown interest in
my work and who have encouraged me to
perform and to share with a larger audience.

Poems, songs, raps, and music are ways to
communicate and express ourselves,
and I've learnt many things about life
through them.

The beauty is to live the life through
understanding what we have seen,
done, or felt, and all this can be shared
through the stroke of a pen.

Not all of us choose to write, but we can still
share what we feel and bring it to light.

We begin to see more of ourselves in other
people, and to work for the cause to make
all things equal.

The children are the future and they live what they are taught, and it is within the guiltiness of society that they've been caught.

Some are freed and become seeds of light and hope, and through nutritional experiences and cultural variety they slowly begin to cope.

Others get lost and seem full of hate, maybe from some of the things that they have lived or ate.

Try to give a helping hand, because in yours are their fate.

Life has shown me that all children are born innocent and that it is people that create and cause divisions.

Teach respect, peace, love, liberty, social justice, and truth and rights.

These are the virtues that bring out the true equality and harmony of life.

DEDICATION

Dedicated to my mother,
known to family and friends as *Blossom*.

She will always be a part of what
I share with the world.

R.I.P.
(Real Important Person).

THANKS

Special thanks to my brother Milton and all at the SPACE Project who have supported my delivery of poetry to schools and organisations.

Thanks again to Nick Toczek and the team at Caboodle Books Ltd.

CONTENTS

MI EDZ A SHED

Mi edz a shed, it's full of old jumble.
There's books an papers old stair cases,
Still a mustn't grumble.

It's got a couch, a table, an even a bed.
A box full of tools, even barstools,
And pillows to cover mi ed.

There's a bike, a kite, a big spider's web.
Even a barbeque so a can get fed.
Lots of shoes, old blown fuse,
Speakers, tweeters, old amplifiers,
Rusty skates wid worn out tyres.

Mi edz a shed, it's full of dusty places,
Old football boots, old bags of loot;
An pictures wid funny faces.
Mi edz a shed, a can never find things in it,
Or where I even put it.
I have to wonder if someone took it.
A sed mi edz a shed, I shud of stayed in bed.

It really needs a gud clear out.
Well after it waz cleaned it seemed to beam,
But I still can't remember nowt.

WORDZ

Wordz are for everyone,
Everyone to use.
Learn them to speak and even express your views.

Wordz are in everything, in and out of sight.
From A to B and C to Zee, or anything you like.
Every word spoken, lives inside a pen,
Find one in your hand you can soon write them.

Every day you get up you should write a few wordz,
Like if you live on the edge,
Your cheese will fall off your curb.
Or like a foolish dog barks at a flying bird.

Everywhere you go try take a dictionary,
Always leave room for a little one to carry.
Because every now and then,
Or even every time,
A word you never heard,
You can find in no time.

Wordz are for everyone,
Everyone to use.
Learn them to speak and even express your views.

PRETTY SNOW WHITE

Pretty Snow White and di seven dwarfs,
Dem all tek a trip just to see New York.
Singing an dancing, up ina di street.
Everyone came jus to hear dis treat.
Dem sing all night, dem sing all day.
Until it was time, to go away.
Dem jump pan a plane den waved goodbye.
Den di plane disappeared up ina di sky.

JACK'S GOLDEN EGGS

Fee Fi Fo Fum.
Did my nose smell someone?
By my hive of golden eggs,
I saw Jack run with di fastest legs.
He stole my hen and away he ran,
He's cracking my eggs in his frying pan.
I'd get them back if he were caught;
But there no longer is, a GIANT BEAN-STALK!

RIDDLE MI DIS

Riddle mi dis,
Riddle mi dat.
Riddle mi now mi lyrical chat.
Riddle mi av like water from tap.
Riddles in mi toe, ankle an mi knee.
Riddle in mi waist an back an belly.

Riddle in mi chest yes, heart an mi lungs.
Riddle from mi mouth jus a come off a mi tongue.
Riddles weh yu want den, riddles cya dun.
Riddles weh mi got under di blazing sun.

So lyrics a weh yu want den,
Lyrics a weh yu get.
Riddles weh mi av you get dem live an direct.
Like watch a weh mi wear is a seko mek.
It tell mi di hour yo minutes and di sec.
Listen fimi lyrics dem fast like a jet.

To run session is my mission
All over da place dem call Inglan.
Mi nuh born mi nuh grow, mi seh dung a Landan.
My madda christen mi Donavan.

Riddle mi dis riddle mi dat,
Riddle mi now mi dun mi rap!

YU SI MI

Embrace mi love mi
Du nuh badda diss mi.
Check mi riss mi
Please nuh badda lick mi.
Guide mi help mi
Du nuh badda fool mi.
Show mi teach mi
But don't try rule mi.
Nuh fight mi nuh spite mi
Sum seh dem nuh like mi.
Dem never talk to mi,
Seh dem hear bout mi.

Nuh seh yu discover mi, or find mi,
Wen yu seek yu wi find;
Mi dehya long time.
Well now yu simi;
How yu fi know mi.
Why not jus try talk to mi.

Anyway dats enough about mi.
Believe mi an excuse mi.
Wat I would like to know,
Before I have to go.
Please tell mi
Who are you?

RAPPAMAN

R to da A to da PP A

Rappaman iz here today.
To show you how, to rhyme an rap.
Write nuff wordz jus like dat.
Pick up yu pen an thinking cap.
Pen an paper start to chat.

R to da A to da PP A
Donavan C iz here today.
Showing luv an nuff risspek.
Nuff risspek, iz wat you get.

R to da A to da PP A
Wordz in work, rest an play.
Like W to da O to da R an K,
R to da E to da S an T,
P to da L to A an Y.

Wordz are like a fountain, gone up to the sky.

R to da A to da PP A
Rapper rap rap till yu old an grey.

Don't diss-risspek wat I say,
Because wordz will help u along life's way.

VOiCES AN THOUGHTS

Voices and thoughts laid down in ink.

Letters an wordz to make people think.
A poem iz like a table waiting to be set,
Jus like the ink jus after it iz wet.
Line after line the table iz arrayed,
Slowly but surely the table iz laid.

Wordz are served with a black ladle.
Delicious spicy brain food, on your table.
Introduce delicatessens for your starters,
Or sometimes wine, soup, stout or juice,
A little tea or coffee to mek yu feel spruce.

The main course iz the content of what yu eat.
Some wordz are dear, some wordz are cheap.
The wordz you eat are the wordz you speak.
Some wordz are vegetables,
some wordz are meat,
Some wordz are horrible, some wordz are sweet.

Desert for conclusion, ice cream or spongy pud,
Custard for inclusion, it all tastes gud.
A table laid forever, no sell by date,
Jus a feast full of wordz to decorate yu plate.

Yu can digest more;
If yu use your skill.
For this meal there iz no bill.
Because every time you read;
You'll get your full fill.

RISSPEK MI RISSPEK

Risspek mi risspek
Jus like you should.
Yu wah Risspek
But act like a thug.

Risspek mi risspek
Spen a likkle time.
And don't mek yu face look
Sour like lime.

Risspek iz gud, Risspek iz true
Risspek iz sumting we should all do.

If wi don't love and show Risspek,
The whole of the world will be ship-wrecked.

Risspek mi risspek
Jus like yu should.
Yu wah Risspek
But act like a thug.

Some seem to forget what iz Risspek.
Risspek's from the heart, before the mouth.
Risspek's not to push and shove me about,
Or turn around and give me a clout.

Teasing, stealing, verbal abusing.
Granny scaring, it's not amusing.
Fire starting, property burning,
Stone throwing, window breaking.

People hurting, people crying,
People lying, people dying,
If yu diss, yu should be ashamed.
Because diss iz not part of the Risspek game.

Risspek mi risspek
Jus like yu should.
Yu wah Risspek
But act like a thug.

Risspek mi risspek
Spen a likkle time.
And don't mek yu face look
Sour like lime.

11

P.O.E.T.R.Y.

(Positive Oral Expression Through Reciting Yourself)

Well this is P. O. E. T. R. and a Y.
I'll be slinging wordz like this,
Till the day that I die.
P. O. E. T. S. poet's time.
It's time to communicate, to the people wid a rhyme.

Say from the day that you're born,
In case you never know it.
Everybody's got a skill to be a lyrical poet.

Everybody wants to talk,
Everybody wants to rap.
Nobody wants to lose;
Or even get da sack.
So if you start from A and set your mind free,
You can go, you can flow, jus like me.

Some of my sentences are long flowing like a river Nile.
Some are jus short, oh my!

Well this is P. O. E. T. R. and a Y.
I'll be slinging words like this,
Till the day that I die.
P. O. E. T. S. poet's time;
It's time to communicate to the people wid a rhyme.

I believe everyone was born to be a poet,
Everybody's got a skill, they jus don't know it.
But every time you speak you begin to show it.
Jus listen to your wordz, as you begin to flow it.

Positive Oral Expression Through Reciting Yourself.
It's good for your brains, and it's good for your health.

Well this is P. O. E. T. R. and a Y.
I'll be slinging wordz like this,
Till the day that I die.
P. O. E. T. S. poet's time;
It's time to communicate to the people wid a rhyme.

BADNESS A MADNESS

Instead of having a fight, I've learned to jus write.
Now since then all ma days have been sunny an bright.
I realised ma pen's a glove that knocks out hate,
And brings forth love.

I remember ma old skool bully, used to push an shove,
Till ma pen knocked im out,
And taught him some love.
He also thought he waz really bad.
But deep down inside, ma pen knew he waz sad.
So ma pen took im on, one on jus one;
And taught him a valuable lesson.
Now a call him a fren, a very good fren.
Instead of telling im to stop messing.

A sed.
Wouldn't yu rather be kool, instead of being a fool?
Wouldn't yu rather jus kool?
Instead of being cruel?
Cruel to yu brother an cruel to yu sister an yu sister is a girl,
Jus like yu mother.
An I am like you; that's why I call you brother.

Brother do yu hear mi, do yu understand,
The time has come to represent, one day you'll be a man.
The table's gonna turn, gonna turn one day.
The wicked an the cruel, will get their pay.
So yo! yo! yo! Remember weh mi say.
Badness a madness an play a jus play.

RULEZ RULEZ RULEZ

Rulez in skool, Rulez pan di street.
Seems everywhere mi go;
A bare Rulez mi meet.

Rulez fimi house
An Rulez wen mi go out.
Rulez pan wall
Rulez pan paper,
Rulez dem give yu, wen it too late sa.

Rulez fi Woman, Rulez fi Man.
Sum Rulez deh bout; mi can't overstand.
Rulez fi you, Rulez fi me.

Rulez yu kyan see;
And Rulez yu can't s
Rulez fi PEACE an Rulez fi war.
More Rulez, fi make
Fi keep di world in ShApE.
Rulez fi day an Rulez fi night.

An still;
Not all RuleZ are in black an white.

LAZY TOM

Sleepy Tom was oh so lazy.
He lounged around
On the basis of daily.
Tom would never go to school.
He'd rather play
And be Tom fool.

He never not ever
Even read a book.
Nor ever even took a look.
He never wrote a single thing,
At night he'd hang out and sometimes sing.
With his mates through the gates
off they'd roam,
And by early morning he'd always be home.

Mum never really seemed to be bothered.
If it were me, I would have been clobbered.
He'd eat, yawn and sleep in the flat,
I suppose I'd do the same if I were a cat.

BLESSED WITH SKILL

Our Head Teacher is really brill
Talented, sophisticated
Blessed with skill.
She walks the walk, talks the talk.
Multitasks very fast and well multi skilled.

When we're playing futty an short of a player.
She'll always turn out as our best left-winger.
Slicky an tricky
Two quick feet.
With instant ease, three players she beats.

Oversteps, stepovers, even windmills.
Pace and power and blessed with skill.
A touch of finesse and a shot like a rocket.
I don't even think Ben Foster could stop it.

All the children will stop their play.
To see the Head show her skilful display.
Challenges come in, like it's a battle.
But she glides through the field avoiding
every single tackle.
We shout 'next goal wins!' before we go to dinner.

Before we even know it
She's popped in the winner.
Our Head Teacher is really brill!
Talented, sophisticated
And blessed with skill.

THESE TWO PUPILS

These two pupils in my class,
Seem to stare all day
But learn so fast.

These two pupils rarely speak
But their written work
Is always neat.

These two pupils do everything together.
Everyone thinks they're ever so clever.

These two pupils are always there.
One's always peeping through his hair.

These same pupils in my class,
Seem to look at the world from behind a glass.
At school they never seem to see my face,
Even while we share the same space.

They move like twins and just synchronise,
Because these two pupils are my eyes.

ℲOOD WEB

Breaking Da Link

Because everything in the food web is
Independent an' connected.
If one organism dies
Many others can be affected.

Imagine what would happen if all the rabbits died.
The grass and lettuce
Would all start to thrive.
More lettuce, more slugs
More thrushes above.

Hawks and foxes would reduce in number.
Through lack of food
They would die of hunger.

But they could survive if they were peckish.
They would try eat more chaffinches,
Thrushes and blue tits.
More dormice would be stalked
By the fox and the hawk.

Remember, a chain is only as strong
as its weakest link.
So look out for the planet
Or we'll be extinct.

PHOTOSYNTHESIS

SCIENCE
4 step revision

Listen to the code as I break out and tell:

(1)   Sunlight is captured by palisade cells.
       At the upper surface of the leaves.

Chloroplasts are packed just like beads.

(2)   Carbon dioxide enters and leaves.
Through stomata holes under the leaves.

(3)   Water intake, biomass increase.
       Oxygen leaves to help us breathe.

(4)   Chlorophyll's the pigment that exists
In the chloroplasts that make Photosynthesis.

Learn this equation from your heart.
The **GLUCOSE** becomes a chain
And turns to **STARCH**.

LE. CD. WATER. G/O
1   2   3   4
**LIGHT – ENERGY - CARBON DIOXIDE-
WATER – GLUCOSE – OXYGEN**

RHYMEZ TIMEZ

7x (HOME ALONE)

7 Times I called her / his phone.	$1 \times 7 = 7$
14 times I called her / his home.	$2 \times 7 = 14$
21 days I was home alone.	$3 \times 7 = 21$
28 letters I sent by post.	$4 \times 7 = 28$
And lived on 35 slices of toast.	$5 \times 7 = 35$
Ate 42 orders of jerk chicken roast.	$6 \times 7 = 42$
49 steps I took to the coast.	$7 \times 7 = 49$
56 donkeys I rode on my own.	$8 \times 7 = 56$
Missed 63 messages on my phone.	$9 \times 7 = 63$
70 times it said I'll soon be home.	$10 \times 7 = 70$

RHYMEZ TIMEZ

This is rhymez timez where we develop a time
Table timez we just developing a number
To multiply or timez
Means to add a little quicker
Rhymez timez
Rhymez timez

24

7X JAMAICAN STYLE

7, 14 an 21.

Adi first tree numbers ina diss ya song.

28, 35 an 42.

Adi next tree numbers yu afi pass through.

49, 56 an 63.

Di final number seh dat a 70.

Rhymez Timez style, kool an Easy!

BOOKS R4 EVERYONE

Books are for everyone
Everyone to read.
To mek you learn new wordz!
And mek yu knowledge increase.

Books are for everyone
From an early age.
Like books wid pictures
Mek yu wanna turn a page.

There's fiction, non-fiction, science fiction too.
History and mysteries, fantasies for you.
Inside every book
You can learn something new.

About other people and yourself.
Don't let books catch dust on the shelf.
They stand so lonely in a bookcase.
Please read a book and put a smile on its face.

Books will take you way back in time.
Pages and wordz from the author's mind.
How much can you take, or your imagination hold?
Some of the best books to read are really, really old.

Check out the past, check out the future.
Every book you read is another adventure.
Write your own book! On a computer.
Be a book germ or be a book master.

Books are for everyone, everyone to read,
To mek you learn new wordz and
mek yu knowledge increase.

JUNIOR SKOOL
OVER AND OUT

Junior Skool, Junior Skool,
over and out.
Junior Skool, Junior Skool,
where a got ma first clout.
The bullies had no respect;
for teachers an pupils about.
Some pupils suffered in silence,
afraid to open their mouths.

Wish I didn't have to go to that Skool.
Seems like only some abide by the rule.
While others come and play the fool.
Why play the fools I want to ask?
But am not quite sure what's under their mask.
To listen and learn, is that such a big task?

Junior Skool, Junior Skool,
over and out.
Junior Skool, Junior Skool,
where a got ma first clout.

But who am I, when it's over and out?
A man a woman, or someone to clout?
Education is a must;
there ain't no doubt.
You can't sow stones
and expect gold to sprout.

Negative quotes from peers
never helped the cause,
That's why some of you all ran
and broke Skool laws,
Doors, jaws, bloody the floors,
acted violent like going to wars.
Seems like a civil war right here in Skool.
Students want teachers to chill and just be kool.
While some come with tight upper lip rules.
A don't want the innocent
to become also the fools.

Junior Skool, Junior Skool,
wish it was over and out.
For the attitude the rude,
but leave the learners about.

BY TEN

(Story by numbers)

1 fine sunny day, 2 fishes swam up the river.
3 days they struggled against the tide,
Be 4 they had to stop and decide.
To take a 5 minute break, for their health's sake.

6 fishermen were casting lines,
To catch some fish, before tea time.
And for 7 tough hours, they had tried,
To catch some fish, juicy maggots were the bribe.
As they'd all caught none;
They thought they'd all gone.

So their bread was 8 without the fish.

The fish which swam swiftly, tiredly up the river,
Were hiding in the riverside for some time.
The sun was going down, it was nearly after 9.
They decided to swim up the river agen!
As they had to be home,
Home by 10.

JOURNEY ON A PEN

Wordz won't stop coming out of ma brain.
Out of ma brain, out of ma brain.
Wordz, rolling jus like a train.
Like a train, like a train.

Ma pen's out of ma brain, down through ma vein.
Down to ma fingers for ma pen to write again.
Again another **word**, again another **style**.
Again another **thought**, again another **line**.
I want to **stop** but yu know I cann**ot**.
I'll have to **wait** till this pen drops me **off**.

Pen drops me **off**, at the next **stop**.
Next stop **please** as I talk to ma pen
Faster, faster as ma pen takes a **bend**.
Then all of a **sudden**, it stops a sudden **stop**.
I thought to ma **self,** a better get **off**.
But before I could get off, ma pen it shot off.

Off like a rocket, bullet shooting down ma **page**.
Jus like an actor, dancing on a **stage**.
Ma pen hears the beats of the silent **sounds**.
Before it lets me go it's got to write them **down**.
Ma pen's happy **now**, it's gonna let me **go**;
Because this line says
It's the end of ma floooow!

31

THE FUTURE'S YOURS

It's not your fault things have got so bad,
Got so bad, got so bad.
It's not your fault things have got so bad,
But what can you do?

Seems no peace no love, no love no peace.
When will all this anger cease?

One day the world will belong to you.
What will you do?

Look at your neighbour, look at them now.
Tell me why, tell me how,
Tell me why you want to row?

LLLLLLListen!
Learn to care, learn to share
Learn to understand the apple and pear.
There are lots of different fruits out there.

One day you'll make the rulez, take care.
Make sure, make sure your rulez are fair.

PS PT KOOL?

Yes bless and nuff risspek
Some think it's kool,
To be a fool.
Without any common sense.
Simply because;
Wordz from your mouth,
Never make any sense.

It's kool to say sorry, it's kool to say please
What type of world would we be living in?
If we didn't have wordz like these.

SCRAMBLED HEADS

Skool can be full of Krazy teachers.

Who say "finders keepers, losers weepers."

Skool can be full of Krazy kidz.

Who talk a lot of Krazy fibz.

HUMAN NATURE

It's only human to feel hurt or upset,

That's why we sometimes cry.

Everybody cries, even boys and extra big men.

We are, after all, only human.

I SAY. I SAY. I SAY

Is risspek a name
On a T-shirt or a sweater?
It should be what you already possess.
Everybody wants a little
RISSPEK
If you can't find what you possess, then why not
buy my latest?
RISSPEK PRINTED ON

Shirts
Shorts
Coats an
Caps.
Knickers
Bras
Blouse
Jeans an
Sneakers.
Jackets
Hoodies
Woolly jumpers.
Jogging bots
And jogging tops.

That's all I sell
In mi RISSPEK
Shop.
Den do you think everybody
would have a little more,
RISSPEK?

Life

Is like a monopoly board
That can change to Snakes and Ladders,
At any time in the plot.

The strange thing is that
Everyone's involved.
And you only progress,
When you have a problem solved.

You must have good patience,
As the game can go on for ages.
Pay attention to the rulez;
At all key stages.
You're the book.
You must know;
When to turn the pages.

SHADOWS OF LIGHT

Shadows in the **garden**
Shadows on the **walls**.
Shadows all around **us**
Shadows for **us all**.

Shadows at the **windows**
Who or what could it be?
Shadows at the **door**,
Count them: **one, two, three**.

Shadows below the **leaves**.
Shadows are always **there**,
At the **dark side** of the **trees**.

Shadows in my mind
That's all I seem to **see**.
Shadows on the **land** and shadows over **sea**.

Shadows live in **prisons**.
Shadows live in **shade**.
Shadows never see the light,
But it's from light **shadows** are made.

WHAT SHALL WI EAT

Food food, what shall wi eat?
I like lots of food, can wi call food sweets?
If food were sweets I'd eat them all day long.
I'd have to look after my teeth or
they'd soon be all gone.

But sweets are not food, that's what I've been told.
If yu eat the right food, you'll have teeth till you're old.
32 teeth if yu do the right sums,
Milk, yoghurt, cheese: equals calcium.

Food food, what shall wi eat?
Proteins and iron, from fish an meat.
Got to eat proper, got to eat sensible.
So eat some roots and a likkle vegetable.

Yu body needs fibre and vitamins.
No need for some tablets or some medicines.
Carbohydrates and energy is what yu body needs.
For a healthy mind and body if yu want to succeed.
Am not a vegetarian, I pick an choose mi meat.
Sunday roast, Yorkshire pud or pie an peas.
It's all so goody gud, I like all of these.

So if yu wanna stay healthy yu got to eat food.
Because if yu don't eat you'll be ina bad mood.
Grumpy, upset and feeling miserable.
So eat proteins and a likkle vegetable.

Food food, what shall wi eat?
Anyting you like jus eat it like a treat.

FOOD, BEAUTIFUL FOOD

Food is for everyone, from veg to meat.
Especially gud for you wen yu belly starts to beat.
Yu got to eat food seven days of the week.
Do a likkle fasting wen yu go to sleep.
Hungry in the morning after mi yawning.
Mi clock's been bawling from seven thirty past.
Wash mi face, brush mi teet before breakfast.

Cornflakes or Weetabix an four slice a toast.
But eggs, beans an plantain a wah mi like di most.
Keep mi going keep mi flowing, till it's time for lunch.
But some people afi stop an have a likkle brunch.
Lunch time a 12 o'clock, more food pan di dot,
Chicken an rice an some cold sour sap.
Anyway, so wi stay nuh feel no way,
Ca everybody eat food ina different way.
Later on a dinnertime, some might call it tea.
Fluids fi yu dinner, well dat is not fi me.
Yam an sweet potato, dumpling an choe choe,
Ackee an salt fish wi national dish.
Nutriment or fruit punch wi jus call it juice.
Den mi ketch a likkle nap, some might ketch a snooze.

Last ting a night mi afi get mi supper.
A hot cuppa choc lit an 2 slice a bread and butter.
Den mi garn straight to bed, at thirty past ten.
An mi cya wait fi morning, fi start eat agen.

CRY OF THE WILDERNESS

I cried the day the landscape died.
The landscape cried,
The landscape cried.
I cried the day the landscape died.
I heard the landscape cry.

Hi-tech revolution commerce wid new solutions
Flattening civilisations and blocking out di light.

I used to come here to see nature play,
Now the birds' high rise apartment,
has become a billboard display.

Magpies with hard hats,
fluorescent jackets an boots.
As they search out the building sites
searching for the loot.

The badger, the beaver, rabbit,
fox and the hare.
They used to come to look for me;
But now they're no longer there.

I cried the day the landscape died.
The landscape cried,
The landscape cried.
I cried the day the landscape died.
I heard the landscape cry.

The owls in the old farm barn,
You know are no longer there.
Mechanical teeth turned me
into a valley of grief;
Naked, they stripped me bare.

The life within my land surround,
Some died, some left, some even drowned,
They cast my clothes around.

They flattened my face
Scattered me all over the place,
I am lost and can never be found.

I tried to fight them back with rocks,
As they dug through my tummy.
But like goldstones they took the lot.
And drove them off to the quarry.

43   poem continues...

I cried the day the landscape died.
The landscape cried,
The landscape cried.
I cried the day the landscape died.
I heard the landscape cry.

As buildings go up I slowly lose my voice,
To the sound of steel and concrete.
An some type of inhumane noise.

Part of me died again,
In travail without a choice.
Until this day I still remain,
A prisoner without a voice.

I cried the day the landscape died.
The landscape cried,
The landscape cried.
I cried the day the landscape died.
I heard the landscape cry.

R YOU MAKING RUBBISH?

Rubbish making grubbish, all day long.
Trash is what they call it, it sings a dirty song.
It used to have a home, to someone it belonged.
Before it was just thrown, now the ground it is upon.
Like a grimy drifter, it drifts all around.
And every day it tussles with the grubbish on the town.
Sneaking in your gardens, then hiding in your hedge.
It joins more littering, rolling into bed.
Hiding in your yard, hiding in the school,
With all this rubbish around, how can the place be kool?

Kool is stush; criss and neat.
Kool ain't rubbish and it don't smell sweet.
Shovel it, sweep it, put it in a bin.
This is a war, it just can't win.

So this is what we'll do just for you, and you, and you.
We'll put you in the bin if you drop litter too.
So if the bin is the place where we put rubbish in,
Don't be surprised where you end up if you keep littering.

NUMBER 6
UP THE STREET

Number 6 up the street is a house made of sweets.
The house made of sweets looks like a nice treat.
If you're in my neighbourhood,
you should really go and see it.

Bricks of chocolate stuck with toffee.
The doors are caramel and smell well jolly.
The windows wobble so they must be jelly.
The satellite dish and even the telly.

Marshmallows for the beds, plus tables and chairs,
A spiral curly-wurly snakes up the stairs.
All the drapes are wafers on liquorice sticks,
Decorated with candy and sherbet pips.
The kitchen and the bathroom are made of cake,
And when you turn on the taps, you get milk shake.
The floors are made of biscuit, the lamp shades too.

Hold on a sec, someone's eaten the loo.
The backdoor, the kitchen and the ceiling.
And depleted the tank with the milk shake in.
When I got back home mum was standing there.
She looked curious with a glaring stare.
Where have you been,
and what have you been doing?

"Nowhere, Mum," I said, "Am just coming in."
She looked at me and ma face had a grin.
She said, "Excuse me, what's this on your chin?"
There was chocolate and toffee, caramel and jelly.
A piece of the telly and a part of the loooo.
Liquorice and biscuit, you know I had to risk it
I wasn't gonna miss this,
What would you do?

The house made of sweets was a house up the street.
So the house up the street was a house I had to eat.

PEN MARRIES BLANK PAPER

Blank paper became a bride,
When I never had anything to write.
I just introduced my pen to the blank paper.
The pen did the rest.
It spoke of how the paper was blank and bare.
And had no structure.
So my pen decided to marry
This blank sheet of paper.

I was there at the wedding.
I was the best man and held the ring.
The pen kissed the paper.
The paper cried:
She never ever thought she'd be
A beautiful blushing bride.

Now as you can see, they're in harmony,
Together side by side.

She was once blank and bare,
But now she's full of a rhyme.
When she thought no one cared,
Along came this pen of mine.

LUCKY HUMPTY

I went back in time
To seek and find.
The wall that Humpty Dumpty sat on.
Blew it up with a gong!
Then it was gone.
Now the children will sing a new song.

Like Humpty Dumpty went to the park.
Played all day till it was dark.
Then all of a sudden, saw a big bright spark.
Bright as sunshine, it lit up the park.
Someone has blown up the park wall.
The one he dreamt of when he was small.
The one where he was supposed to fall.

All of sudden he saw the Queen's men.
Horses an-all, hundreds of them.
Charging, rushing, trumpeting sounds.
Like a heeeeerd of ELEPHANTS,
they shook the ground.

Humpty Dumpty ran like a cat,
Out of the park he did dash,
Ran through the streets and fell in the trash.
Disturbed a dog, distressed a rat.
Humpty Dumpty took off like a bat.
Now I don't know just where he's at.

But all the Queen's horses and all the Queen's men
Put the wall back together again.

GUESS WHAT
I'VE SEEN

Lizards in caps and dark glasses.
Lizards with books, sitting in classes
Lizards with wallets and bus passes.
Lizards in the playground, chasing the lasses.

Lizards with loot, hiding their stashes.
Lizards in jeans, dungarees with patches.
If you believe me, you must be CRACKERS!

TING A LING A LING

Ting a ling a ling.
School bell a ring.
Chue we a play, wi nuh wah go in.

Ting a ling a ling.
Now wi hiding.
When mi tek a look, everybody smiling.

Ting a ling a ling.
Yu know sumting.
Dat is the smell of granny cooking.

Ting a ling a ling.
A serious ting.
Last one in don't get no pudding!

DO ME A RAP

(This is a call and response rap reply six times)

Rapper man, rapper man, please do a rap.
If I do a rap, can you clap?
Clap clap clap, clap clap clap.

Rapper man, rapper man, rap it up quick.
If I rap it up quick, can you click?
Click click click, click click click.

Rapper man D.C. please do a rhyme.
If I do a rhyme, shout "yo" six times
YO YO YO, YO YO YO.

R to the A to the P. **RAP!**
I better keep flowing,
You said you'd clap, if I did a rap.
Clap clap clap, clap clap clap.

Rapper man, rapper man
Do one again.
Do one again, listen this again.

Abc defg hijklm, NO PQ rstu vwxy zed.

Rhymez keep rolling around my head.
Wrote a rhyme last night, before I went to bed.
I scribbled and I scratched, ma pencil ran outta lead.
I thought I'd do a rap, to boost mi street cred,
But when I woke in the morning, ma page was full a zedz
Zedz, zedz zedz z z zedz z z zedz z z zed.

Rapper man, rapper man, please do a rap
If I do a rap, can you clap?
Clap clap clap, clap clap clap.

I did this rap, especially for you
Now turn to someone and say **RISSPEK DUE!**

CHATTER RAP

**(Groups respond to shout rap!
after r to the a to the p is said)**

R to the A to the P.　　**RAP!**
　　We better get going.
R to the A to the P.　　**RAP!**
　　Read a poem.

R to the A to the P.　**RAP!**
　Do you see what I see?
R to the A to the P.　**RAP!**
　Rhyme and poetry.

R to the A to the P.　**RAP!**
　No use not knowing.
R to the A to the P.　**RAP!**
　Real attitude poems.

R to the A to the P.　**RAP!**
　Smile with a dimple.
R to the A to the P.　**RAP!**
　Respect all people.

R to the A to the P.　**RAP!**
　Can you rhyme properly?
R to the A to the P.　**RAP!**
　Rhythmic African poetry.
R to the A to the P.　**RAP!**

DIFFERENT

Who decides what different is like?
Are we sure of wrong and right?
To be different is a strange thing.
If you really know what different is like.
But who decides what different is like?
What's different: Brown, Black or White?

For you to know I'm different,
You must be different too.
So who's different, difficult,
Is it me?
Or is it you?
But do I complain, no I refrain,
From trying to be like you.
That makes me different, difficult,
For not trying to be like you.

Many are called, called are many,
The chosen only a few.
So let's try to compromise,
My wrong could be your right.
But I don't care who's different.
Is it
Brown, Black or White?

IF WE FAIL

If we fail to realise the needs of the individual.
Then we haven't looked at all.
If we fail to spot the character of sadness and laughter
Then we haven't looked at all.

If we fail to show compassion and love,
Then maybe, we have never known love at all.
If we fail to show guidance: spiritual or physical,
Then we haven't cared at all.

If we fail to strive for truth and rights,
Then the writing be on the wall.
If we fail, if we fail, if we fail, if we fail.
A wonder what the future has install.

Maybe no peace, no law, jus war and more.
If we fail to realise,
jus try looking through someone else's eyes.

If we fail to play our part,
Then we have failed on woe mankind behalf.
Don't get lef ina di dark,
time to mek a new start.
Because the future draws near,
I want you all to hear.
If we fail to give a helping hand,
Then you might as well cut off your hand.
Better still jus leave this land.

THe ReFUGe seeKeR

Refugee asylum seeker,
The noise I hear from every corner,
Corners filled with hate and anger.

Again no sleep for the refuge seeker.
You might az well be a biblical leper.
They would give you a place outside their border,
Still making sure they kept things in order.

At least they would keep their distance.
A peaceful night's sleep without the violence.

Refugee asylum seeker.

"Why do you come?
For you here there is no future."
It sounds like something I still remember.
Those ancient voices used to call uz nigger.

My blood runs cold, my bones shudder.
From the dark abusive days my parents still suffer.
I waz also persistently, verbally, racially, abused.
We had to walk in crews, not in ones or twos.

Refugee asylum seekers
No sleep again tonight watching win-ders.
Someone tell mi.
What's changed in the last fifty-odd years?
Racial abuse still brings violence and fears.
With mothers', children's and fathers' tears.

Please check your past and his story,
You might find a family of refugees,
In the branches of your family tree.

And one of those could well be
Me.

PLANET OF THE FOOLS

Imagine this, what if I were you and you were me?
Then you would see the things I see.
Feel the hurt within I feel, maybe you can explain.

Why do some judge by exterior shades?
Should we then judge them by the shades of their hair?
Or by the eyes they wear?
Blue, green, hazel, even black or brown a pair.
Just like the ones I wear.

It's time to open up those eyes.
To open the mind from being blind.
You know and I know we're all one of a kind.

Look around - the world's not square: it's totally round.
There's a world full of interesting shades to be found.
What if we couldn't see shades of colour?
Would we still wanna fight one another?

Well try seeing a world without those shades of colour.
That's a world I wouldn't want to discover.
So don't turn our world into that time and place.
Don't forget, we're all hanging out here in space.

We all push fuel into our face,
Which turns into proteins and carbohydrates.

If it was not so, we would end up like waste.
And of people on earth there would be no trace.
What if I were you and you were me?
Then you would see the things I see.

OLAUDAH EQUIANO

Olaudah Equiano, a black literacy hero.
As a slave he learned to read and write.
And with his pen he began the fight.

Olaudah was captured from his village.
This eleven-year-old boy was not no savage.
Taken in slavery through the middle passage.
Can you imagine how he would have managed?

He spent some time in the West Indies,
Before being sold for unreasonable fees.
To a Virginia planter then a naval officer,
Who renamed Olaudah, Gustavus Vassa.

He had worked those days for his slave master.
Throughout the continent of North America.
After ten years he was free of course.
Apparently as a present he was first bought.

After buying his freedom he was free.
To talk of how to abolish slavery.
He learned to read an' also write,
With his pen he began the fight.

He spoke of the European slave trade.
From his point of view as a slave.
To the House of Lords he even wrote,
How the chains of slavery must be broke.
A letter was sent to the Secretary of State.
That Africans should never, ever face such a tragic fate.

He was the first black author to write to the Queen.
To abolish slavery which was un-pristine.
He even got his books published.
About how the chains of slavery should be abolished.

Olaudah Equiano, a black literacy hero.
As a slave he learned to read and write.
And with his pen he began the fight.

ARAWAKS

Arawaks, Arawaks Indian tribes,
Down in Jamaica's sunny paradise.

Back in time across the Caribbean Sea,
Let's take a look what Columbus did see.
Brown skinned people ruled by a chief.
The law maker, judge and the high priest.

Originally from Venezuela,
made their homes in Jamaica.
They all had gazed, all in wonder,
at these tall-looking strangers.
Why do they come, are they in danger?

The men caught fish and
gave them honey from bees.
And made canoes from tall cedar trees.
Hot pepper pot was their favourite dish.
Hotter the nicer was their wish.

They ate good meals three times a day.
From large pots, made of clay.
The women prepared all the food,
Men built houses, strong and weather-proof.

Arawaks, Arawaks Indian tribes,
Down in Jamaica's sunny paradise.
Back in time across the Caribbean Sea,
Let's take a look what Columbus did see.

Brown skinned people ruled by a chief.
The law maker, judge and the high priest.
These are just some of the things
To show how the Arawaks lived like kings.

POWER UNWRITTEN

The unwritten poem can be
Lying there for days, weeks, months, years.

The power of thought a sign.
Like an embryo caught in a vision of time.
Stored in safety deep in the mind.
Waiting to be written at the writer's discretion.
Sometimes a word can be a whole New World.

Not before time
The table is laid in due process.
Pen and paper start to caress.
The hand will flow and start to express.

The power of thought,
Brought to life;

Simply because we choose to write.

GOING GREEN

Going, going, going green
To keep our earth nice and clean.
How green can you get?
Are you playing your part yet?
Respect goes out to the environment.
To keep the earth green, is our intent.
Recycle people and their mind.
If they're thuggish, make them kind.
If they're dull then make them shine.

Power to the people, energise the night.
Turn off your chargers, TV and lights.
Recycle paper, bottles and tins.
It says "recycle" on your green bins.
Save all the trees and plant some, please.
Try roots, fruits and sweet peas.
Lots of flowers, for the honey bees.
And please don't forget to plant lots of greens.
Turn off standby on your TV set,
If you're not ready to use it yet.
The world would be a safer place, I bet.
To recycle people, instant success.
How green can you get?
Are you playing your part yet?
Going, going, going green,
to keep our earth nice and clean.

67

TO BE OR NOT TO BE

I can be, you can be
Anything you want.
An astronaut, the king of sport,
Even a judge in court.

The captain of the ship,
Or the master of the port.
A general in the army,
Or bringing thieves to court.

One thing I'll never be,
I'll never be a nought.

A doctor or a surgeon or even a nurse.
Just come to me if you're ill, or feeling worn or worse.

A teacher, a preacher or an engineer.
Maybe make scary movies,
Or buildings disappear.

A builder, designer like an architect.
Even at school it was my best subject.

A prime minister, executive, the next President.
That would be too easy as I'm too intelligent.
A writer, researcher or a star on a stage.
One thing I'll never be is a blank page.

Life is what you live,
And life is what you make it.
Don't be such a siv,
And go around and fake it.

You can do it, you can make it
Make it if you try
If you really want it, set your standards high.

RESPECT AND HONOUR

First show honour to yourself,
Then you can honour everybody else.

Respect and honour are like twins,
When they collide, no one wins.
Respect and honour should never be removed.
They should only be improved.

Respect and honour, the foundations from the dirt.
If they should disappear,
So shall the Earth.

Respect and honour
Should reflect from you.
In every step you take,
In everything you do.

Respect and honour
Teach it to all.
Else the stars from the sky
Will surely fall.

Respect and honour: the lost outposts.

Battling for survival
So we don't become ghosts.

Respect and honour
Grow dignity, integrity,
Goodwill, compassion and understandings.
Respect and honour grow all these things.

Respect and honour
A royal vesture of steel.

Respect and honour
Let's keep it real.

First show respect to yourself
Now you can respect everybody else.

IN NEED OF A CURE

Many hands and the work is done,
All before the setting of the sun.
But too many chiefs cause confusion.
So check the balance of your solution.
Sorry, excuse me, thanks and please,
What would the world be without these?
A little advice is better than none,
Or do you wanna be lastminute.com?

Time is free for the use of the land,
Time can be just where you stand.
Time you can find on your hand,
Still time is what some never understand.
So listen to learn,
But first learn to listen;
Know your purpose, goals and mission.
Dreams can be reality seen in a vision.

If you're not sure then you must ask,
A poem to guide you through this task.
Life is real and what you make it,
Days can't be replaced if you fake it.
Work hard to what you want to be,
And never be a wannabe.

We're all made up of different fractions,
So be responsible for all your actions.
Whenever someone of you is doubtful,
Stay calm, be true and keep respectful.
If you fail to get down, then get down to fail,
Please know the facts don't follow a tale.

If there was no light we'd all look the same,
But as the sun rises above we all show our shame.
Thirst everyday for a little more knowledge,
Please don't treat this like sloppy porridge.

So life has taught me that's for sure;
That these things, not presumption,
are better than the cure.

A NIGHT TO SIGHT

Ina instance[1] the silence was broken.
Jack Frost danced on slanted slated rooftops,
Smoke was adrift slow motion in the air,
Glimmering, shimmering,
moonlight was cast - everywhere.

Ice cold fires decorated the sky,
while frosty air stands ground upright.
Through sea of air, geese migrate in flight.
Hawk and talk, flap and squawk,
over above our down below.
Arrowed in sequence a sight of elegance,
over above our down below.

When flail of wings fade away, for instance
The silence of night returns from a distance.
Command returned to the full moon on high.
The aura of its power shall never be denied.
Smoggy filled air, slowly vaporised,
As a genie from its bottle,
way up into the heights.

1: 'Ina instance' is used in Jamaica to mean 'in an instant'.

The glimmering, shimmering,
which was cast everywhere,
Slowly retreated into their lair.
By crack of morn, the moon had seemed
to have forgotten its way.
As the sunrise arrived it seemed to stay.
But was reminded by the sun: it's my turn to play
So off over the horizon, it slinks and shrinks away.
Ina instance;
The silence was broken today.

INTO THE DARK

**(The children can make the sounds they hear
starting when they hear a shrieeek!)**

Into the night, into the dark
The dark, dark night.
Things will creep, some will walk
While others take to flight.

When darkness falls, life it begins
Air, land and sea all type a things.
Walking, crawling, some with wings
Bites and scratches, some with stings.

A thousand legs and forty feet
Hide your heads under sheets.
Not even the brave will take a peep.
Filled with dread and filled with grief.
Knocking knees and chattering teeth.
Tonight the dead will walk and speak.

Into the night into the dark
The dark, dark night.
Things will creep, some will walk
While others take to flight.

Is my heart racing, or did it miss a beat?
Through the dark, out of the night,
Did you hear a SHRIEEEK!?

Oh my, oh my, oh me, fear is all around of me,
Tonight feels like a week and I'm bursting for a pee.
Is it getting colder, who turned off the heat?
Shu shu shu be quiet, am sure I heard a CREAK!

Am not sure what I heard it might have been a SQUEAK!
Did you hear that Thomas? It sounds like lots of SHEEP!
I don't know, I can't hear; am pretending to be asleep.
Yo! You better wake up, I can hear marching feet!

Into the night into the dark
The dark, dark night.
Things will creep, some will walk
While others take to flight.

Am calling those busters pass me your cell phone
That's not a shriek or a squeak, am sure I herd a groan!
Am like a fly in a bottle, where darkness fills the jar.
Am I hearing lots things, did someone just go Aaaargh!?

Into the night into the dark
The dark, dark night.
Things will creep some will walk.
While others take to flight.

BLACK CINDERELLA

(PEFORMANCE POETRY STYLE)

Where can I find 'My Black Cinderella?'
I've got to find 'My Black Cinderella'
Cinderella, she lose ar cultcha.
She get teef out of a muma AFRICA.
But here comes di prince AFRICAN warrior.
Cultcha ina han, deh ask all woman.
Which Cinderella could dis culture belong?

Some adem a say it belong to Mary Ann.
No, No way she tek size 91.
Gud gosh! Woman a weh yu get yu size from?

Buckup ina house ina di Caribbean.
An every weh mi go Woman a look attention.
A squeeze an a squeeze, dem fut smell a cheese,
Mi afi say cease, mek di culture ketch breeze.

Wen mi tek a stop a saw a pretty lady.
She say dat culture it belongs to me.
An wen mi check it out it fit ar fut easy,
Mi bawl, Cindy Cindy, will yu marry me.
A saw yu in da dance an yu drove mi krazy.
Wen 12 o'clock struck, a took a likkle look;
Yu was garn in dem boats like sum teef an crook
Cinderella; a wanna give back yu culture.
I've got to find; my; black cinder;..reh..el..la la la la.

THE HONEYMOON

The pen and the paper, pen and the paper
Took a honeymoon.
They left in September, last year September
They said they'd be back very soon.

They had no money to take a cruise.
They had no money to take a flight.
They had nothing left but to choose;
They made themselves into a kite.

Jumped off the cliff of lovers' leap
And flew off into the night.
Who said the price of love is steep,
As a private jet their very own flight.

They haven't returned these many moons.
People have looked for them in hot air balloons.
They sent me a postcard asking if I was free.
And if I was they'd be coming for tea.

They also said they'd be passing by.
Look for them in the moonlit sky.
They were looking some work which was kool,
Wanted to speak to children in skools.

They flew in last night from Montego Bay.
So I've brought them here for you today.
Tomorrow I must bid them on their way.
This is the paper that married the pen,
On their way home from Jamaica.

They'd just like to say
Big up and risspek, one luv everybody.
Take care and be kool nuh badda wid nuh fally.
Don't loaf out yu days an don't dilly dally.
Wen pen meets paper, dem must afi marry.

TRANQUIL

I see the ferocious ferocity,
I see the source of power.
Enraged from out of the moment,
In a second of the hour.
In an instant we're enraged.
Darkness engulfed arrives to devour.

As buffaloes racing across the sky,
The firmament's forming, forms from above.
It covers the scape like a shroud;
Like you can't escape from its murky crowd.

A picture in a flash is taken.
The walls begin to stand up tall.
Am I to be left, forsaken?
As they crash like wreckage, when they fall.
Souls yonder whistle their distant cry,
As they seem to pass to bid me goodbye.

I see the ferocious ferocity,
Caught in the net of the void all around me.
I see the beauty of tranquillity;
In the calm of life at the bottom of the sea.

I WROTE THIS POEM

I wrote this poem for all to share.
I wrote this poem when it seemed no one cared.
I wrote this poem for all nations around.
I wrote this poem looking at the world upside down.

I wrote this poem standing on my head.
I wrote this poem lying on my bed.
I wrote this poem sitting on a chair.
I wrote this poem with a frozen stare.
I wrote this poem travelling on a train.
I wrote this poem from words on my brain.
I wrote this poem about people on earth.
I wrote this poem when I was feeling hurt.
I wrote this poem to make people smile.
I wrote this poem in a different style.

I wrote this poem all about love.
I wrote this poem nobody understood.
I wrote this poem, I felt one was due.
I wrote this poem especially for you.
I WROTE THIS POEM

(Now read this poem from bottom to top)

83

WHEN WE TAKE OUR BREAK

Playground kidz are playing, when we take a break
From the classroom to the yard, we like to escape.
Playing in the playground, jumping rope wid frenz,
Boyz are kicking footballz down the other endz.

Hopscotch in the corner,
use some chalk to mark it out.
Handstandz against the wall,
while some just scream and shout.

Leaping frogz are everywhere,
Girlz playing with their hair,
While jumping frabbits scattering,
An boyz and girlz are chattering.
Others playing tig,
While some just call it tag.
If you can't tig or tag.
It can get you really mad.

The teacher in the playground cast a watchful eye.
They're there in case of injuries.
Or should a child begin to cry.
Playground kidz are playing, when we take a break.
From the classroom to the yard, we like to escape.
Playing in the playground, jumping rope wid frenz,
Boyz are kicking footballz down the other endz.

MISS, THERE'S A FRABBIT

There's a Frabbit in the Skool
There's a Frabbit in the Skool.
Oh my gosh! There's a Frabbit in the Skool.

Did you see it, did you see it?
Did you see its eyes?
Yes I did, course I did, they're big like apple pies.

There's a Frabbit in the Skool
There's a Frabbit in the Skool.
Oh my gosh! There's a Frabbit in the Skool.

Here comes the Head as the news had spread.
As Charles had said!
He was sent to explain to the Head.

Did you say a rabbit Charles?

No I sed a Frabbit Miss.
A Frabbit Charles?
A Frabbit Miss!
What is it?

A Frabbit Miss.

And where is it?
Behind you miss!
Where?
There, just over there.
The Frabbit gave the Head, a great big a scare.

She flew out of her shoes and into the air.
Came down with a thud! And landed in a chair.
But she couldn't do anything to save her hair.
It was all over here and all over there.
Looks like the Frabbit gave her a day-mare!

There's a Frabbit in the Skool
There's a Frabbit in the Skool.
Oh my gosh! There's a Frabbit in the Skool.

Did you see it, did you see it?
Did you see its eyes?
I saw it, yes I saw it and I saw the Head fly.

LEARN SOMETHING NEW

Today's a good day to learn something new,
Like A to the E to the I. O. U.
In every word spelt these letters are found;
Known as vowels in cities and towns.

B to the C to the D, F, G.
H to the J,
K, L, M, N, P.

Q to the R to the S and T.
V to the W, X and Zee.

These letters are the keys.
To spell like the bees.

Consonants are the letters that help words speak.
And through this rhyme, I truly hope to teach.

Y can be a consonant; I can't make it clearer.
But it's also a vowel, now go and ask your teacher.

Today's a good day to learn something new
Like A to the E to the I. O. U.

ANOTHER YEAR,
ANOTHER SKOOL

Am not bothered every tings kool,
Moving up a level to ma new skool.
Most of ma mates will be there,
That's for sure that's all I care.
Still a hope my new skool doesn't have lots of,
Glares, stares, ugly bears, moving chairs,
And lots of stairs.
Still looking forward to ma new skool.
Got mi pen, mi satchel and mi rule.

Mum said wat yu put in is wat yu get out.
Remember Billy Blister, he left skool wid nowt.
He never put owt in,
But still took nuff out.

Like Penny D an Phoney, Bugsy B an Sleepy Slim.
They all left skool wid nowt,
They used to all follow him.
Ma said
Show mi yu company and I'll tell yu who yu are.
Dad said
Think positive if yu wanna go really far.
Still am a little worried but I'll persevere,
Mi future's before mi also mi career.

TEASERS & TWISTERS

THE TEASER 1
What's very angry, made of concrete -
and makes a lot of noise when they meet?

THE TEASER 2
My name sounds like something extinct -
I help you with new ways to think.

THE TWISTER 1
Try saying these as fast as you can.
How do you Expect -
to get Respect from everyone,
When you're Never Ever -
Gonna show Respect to anyone?

THE TWISTER 2
Get a bit a butter get a bit a bread.

RIDDLE 1: The crossroads
RIDDLE 2: Thesaurus

GLOSSARY

Ackee	pod type fruit for the Jamaican national dish
Adi	its the
Afi	I have to
An	and
Ar	her/hers
Av	have
Badda	bother
Bare	a lot of
Bawl	cry
Bout	about
Buckup	a chance meeting
Cho-cho	vegetable
Chue	because
Cya	can't
Da/di	the
Dat/s	that / that's
Deh	there / where are you?
Dehya	here
Dem	them
Den	then
Dilly dally	waste time
Dis	this
Diss	disrespect
Dung	down
Dun	finish
Du	please
Edz	heads

Glossary Continued

Fally	foolishness
Fi	for / to
Fimi	for me / mine
Fut	feet
Garn	gone
Gonna	going to
Gud	good
Han	hand
Ina	in / in the
Ina instance	in an instant: "in an instance, mi stop di war."
Inglan	England
Iz	is
Jerk	type of seasoning used on meat
Jus	just
Ketch	catch
Kool	cool
Kyan	can
Likkle	little
Luv	love
Ma	my
Madda	Mother
Mek	make
Mi	me / my
Nuff	a large amount
Nuh	don't
Pan	on
Plantain	type of banana you boil or fry
Risspek/riss	respect

Glossary Continued

Sa	Sir
Sed	said
Seh	say
Shud	should
Si mi	see me
Skool	school
Sour sap	sweet fruit found in Jamaica and South America
Sumting	something
Teet	teeth
Tek	take
Tree	three
Wah	want
Wa(t)	what
Waz	was
Weh	where/what
Wen	when
Wi	we/will
Wid	with
Wordz	words
Ya	here
Yam	a type of root food found in hot climates
Yo	hey
Yu	you / your

THE THANK YOU

Thank you all for reading these poems.
I hope these wordz will keep you going.
For it's better to be in the knowing.
To spread risspek and keep it growing.